Knitted.
Marvelou
known.
Chosen.
Oh so loved.
Psalm 139:13-16

Pelia the Marvel

Joystine Hoelker

Cover and interior design by
Justine & Chad Froelker

Illustration by Emily Baker

Pelia the Marvel

Written by
Justine Froelker

Illustrated by
Emily Baker

Meet Pelia, a monarch butterfly.

Her name means marvel of God in Hebrew. Marvel means "wonderful or astonishing thing"!

Do you know what your name means?

Hi! My name is Justine, and I am a butterfly farmer.

Pelia and I are going to tell you her story,
from when she was a very tiny egg to the first
time she flies.

We are going to show
you just how much God
marvels in and loves you too!

Before Pelia was born,
her mother had a long journey.

Monarch butterflies
fly the longest distance
of any butterfly.

Monarchs fly from the mountains
of Mexico in the winter
to as far as the trees of
Canada in the summer.

Their
3,000-mile
flight is
very long
and challenging.

God came even further for you.
God came all the way from Heaven and lived as a man.
His name was Jesus.
And, He was full of love.

Pelia's mother flew many miles
to find the perfect milkweed leaf
to keep her babies safe.

Pelia has 300 to 500 brothers and sisters,
all laid as eggs underneath a leaf.

As small as the tip of a pencil and as beautiful as a
diamond, Pelia has almost everything
she needs inside that tiny egg.
She will just need a little bit of help and love,
from me!

A loved creation of God,
Pelia is enough.

She is made with God's love
and has all she needs, always enough.

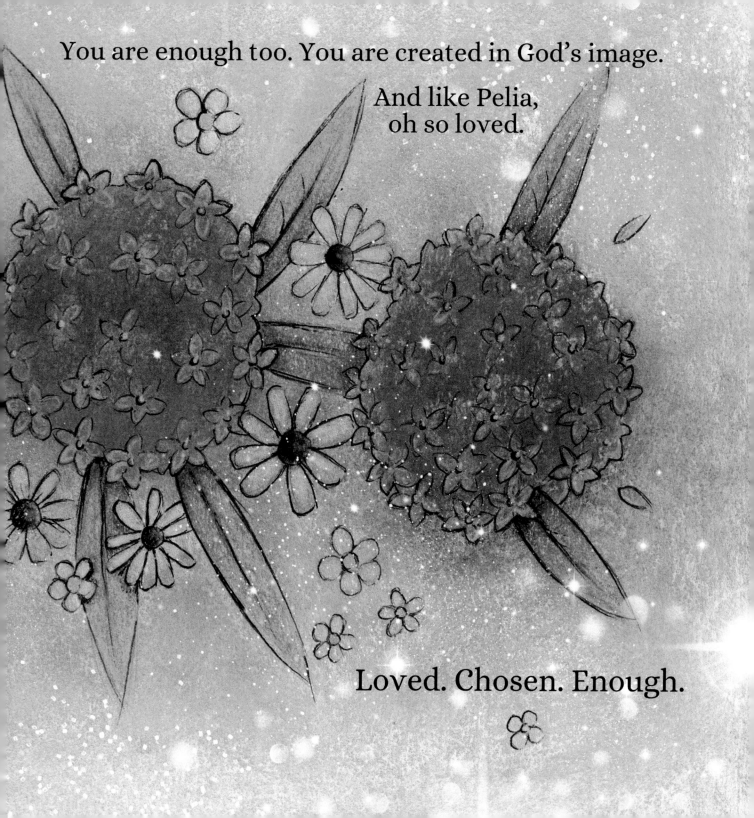

You are enough too. You are created in God's image.

And like Pelia,
oh so loved.

Loved. Chosen. Enough.

In just 5 days, her tiny white egg turns black, which
means Pelia is ready to come out!
Her only way out into the world is to
eat her way out of the egg.
Once her tiny larvae body squeezes out of the egg, Pelia
turns around and eats the egg!
It's her first meal (ewwww)!
She thinks it is delicious though.
She will use it for strength on the journey ahead of her.

Just like Pelia,
you aren't meant to stay tiny either.

You come from God's love, made in His image.
God has amazing plans for you.

Where you come from becomes part of you too.

Trust God and the plans He has for you.
He put Heaven in you.

You are loved.
You are love.

For the next two weeks, Pelia only has three things to do: eat, poop, and grow. She will grow to 2,000 times her size!

If she were a human like you, she would grow as big as a school bus!

Quickly, her tiny gray and black body plumps up with yellow and black stripes.

Every day I clean up after her and provide her with fresh, clean milkweed leaves to eat. Because I love her, I make sure she has what she needs every day.

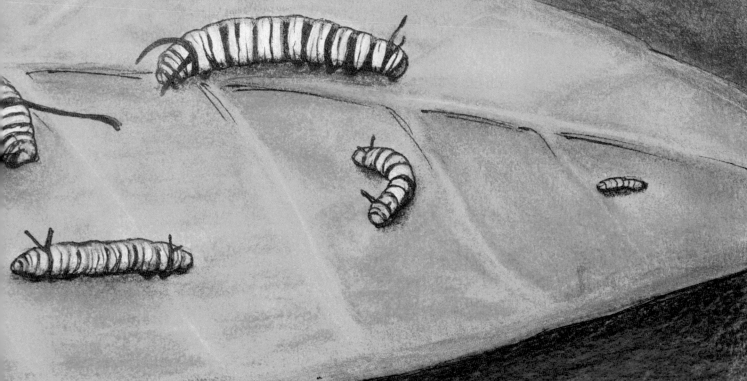

Do you know who loves you even more than I love Pelia?

God.

Every day, God loves you, no matter what.
Every day, God enjoys providing what you need, because you are His child.
Chosen and beloved.

Eating, pooping, and growing comes with a lot of changes. During the next two weeks, Pelia the caterpillar will molt five times.
Molting means she crawls out of her old skin so she can grow bigger. She even loses her face mask every time! And then the grossest part... She eats her old skin! She needs it to grow strong and healthy, because soon she will fly.

Just like Pelia uses that gross skin to help her grow, God will use the fun and the not so fun stuff in your life to help you. God promises to use everything for your good.

God is always by your side.

Simply ask and let Him help.

He will make all things better.

He loves you that much.

After two weeks of eating and growing, a great change awaits Pelia. Soon she will fly!

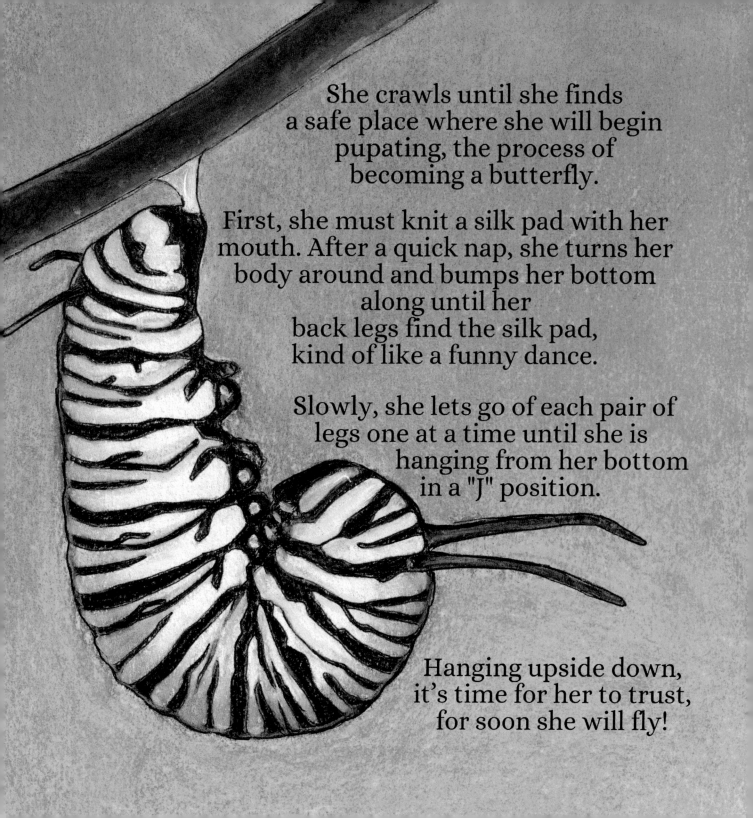

She crawls until she finds
a safe place where she will begin
pupating, the process of
becoming a butterfly.

First, she must knit a silk pad with her
mouth. After a quick nap, she turns her
body around and bumps her bottom
along until her
back legs find the silk pad,
kind of like a funny dance.

Slowly, she lets go of each pair of
legs one at a time until she is
hanging from her bottom
in a "J" position.

Hanging upside down,
it's time for her to trust,
for soon she will fly!

Sometimes it can be confusing when
things feel hard.

It is okay to feel happy and sad at the same time
or to feel like everything is upside down.

Just like Pelia must trust
while hanging upside
down, you can
trust God too.

Jesus knows what it's like
to go through hard times.
He suffered too.

He asked His Father to
take away His hurting.

Yet, He still trusted God.

Jesus understands
how you feel.

Pelia hangs upside down in a "J" for about a day.
During this time, she becomes what I call
a butterfly soup.
Her insides become a soupy goo of
the cells she started with and the cells she needs to fly.
Soon she will straighten out and a tiny bit of bright
green will show on the back of her head.

Unzipping out of her caterpillar skin, she makes her
new home in her jade green and gold chrysalis.
She is in the dark of her own butterfly soup.
She isn't afraid of the dark because she knows she will
soon be able to fly. Pretty soon I will be able to
see her wings!

Sometimes things feel dark before they get better.

When we know Jesus and
remember how much God loves us,
we can trust that God is writing a
beautiful end to our story.

He makes all things good.

God has chosen you.
God came for you.
God loves you so very much.

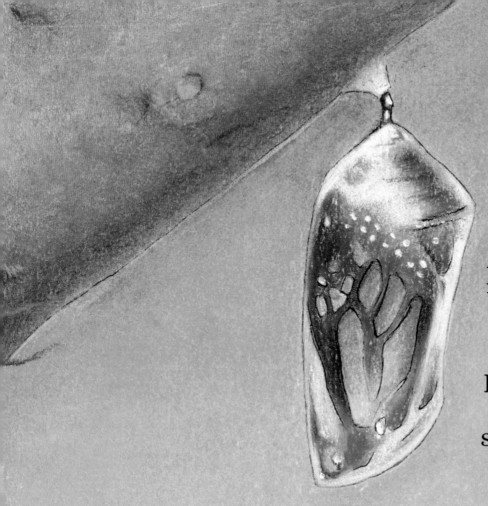

After two weeks
in her chrysalis,
Pelia's orange and
black wings begin
to show through.

Knowing she can't
stay where she is,
she must trust and
come out!

When her chrysalis cracks open, I can see her new
butterfly face.

Somehow, she knows what to do.
Her work isn't done just yet.

It has only been a month and Pelia has eaten her way out of her own egg, molted five times, zipped out of her caterpillar skin, and turned into gooey butterfly soup inside her chrysalis.

She surrendered to come into the world as a beautiful black and orange monarch butterfly, except she still has work to finish.
Next, her tiny orange wings and plump body nearly fall out of the chrysalis as she holds on for dear life with the legs she has never used before.
She must knit together her proboscis to eat from flowers.
She must pump up her wings so she can fly.
She has to choose to be healthy.
Just like we do.

We must also work to take care of ourselves.

Jesus gave us an example of how to
take care of ourselves.

He asked for help.
He asked for prayer.
He rested.

He did the work to be healthy,
and that allowed Him to help many people.

He teaches us to do the same.

Thankfully, He sent a Helper for us.

When Jesus died for you, He left you with a Helper called the Holy Spirit.

The Holy Spirit lives in you and helps you to know what to do every day.

Jesus loved you
so much He died for you
so that one day you can join
Him in Heaven.

The Holy Spirit puts
Heaven inside of you to make
Heaven here on earth through you.

Remember God's
glory and love
are in you.

Pelia is now a butterfly, and she is almost ready to fly.

After four hours of letting her wings expand and dry,
Pelia mightily pumps her wings to let me know
she is ready for her first flight.

She has done so much
work herself.

With lots of love and a
little help from me,
it is now time
for Pelia to fly
into all she is
meant to be.

It is time for
Pelia the marvel to soar.

Prayer:

God, I need you and thank you for forgiving my sins.

Jesus, thank you for loving me so much
you died on the cross for me.

Holy Spirit thank you for being
the Helper I need every day.

God, thank you for never leaving me
and loving me so much.
Amen.

The End

About the Author
Justine Froelker

Justine is a Licensed Professional Counselor with over 20 years of experience in traditional mental health and personal development. She has been certified in the work of Dr. Brené Brown for seven years. Justine is the author of three best-selling books and was also honored to do TEDx Talks at TEDxUMDearborn and TEDxLaSierraUniversity. Currently, she travels nationally delivering keynotes, workshops, and trainings on topics such as leadership, courage, resilience, and much more. Justine lives in St. Louis with her husband Chad, their three dogs, and for four months of the year, hundreds of monarch butterflies.

About the Illustrator
Emily Baker

Emily Baker is a professional illustrator, painter, portrait, and storyboard artist. She earned a Bachelor's degree in fine arts with an emphasis on drawing from Fontbonne University in Saint Louis, Missouri. Emily knew she wanted to be an artist at a young age after watching her mom paint professionally in Los Angeles, California. She currently lives in St. Louis with her husband Paul and two kids, Jun and Lydia.

Acknowledgments

Thank you so much to Emily for bringing to life my Pelia and who God is to me. I am so thankful God brought your spirit, art, and talent into my life. Thank you to Kelli, Kristen, Michelle, Raeleen, and Rebecca for your proofreading and read outloud and mothering to the world skills and gifts to my writing. Thank you, as always, to Chad for believing in me and for helping with design and formatting of all of my books. Most of all, thank you to my community for your support, allowing me to mother you in a holy way, and giving me the honor to show you my Jesus.

Made in the USA
Monee, IL
04 December 2020